AYRSHIRE CATTLE HANDBOOK

The Ultimate Guide for Beginners and Experienced Farmers on Raising, Breeding, Managing, and Profiting From Ayrshire Cattle

CAROLINE D. RENNARD

Contents

Chapter 1

Introduction to Ayrshire Cattle

Ayrshire cattle stand as one of the most respected and enduring dairy breeds in the world, valued for their resilience, efficiency, and adaptability across diverse farming environments. Whether managed by small-scale homesteaders or large commercial dairy operations, Ayrshires have earned a reputation for reliability and balanced performance. This chapter provides a comprehensive introduction to the breed, exploring its origins, global influence, defining traits, and the qualities that make it a compelling choice for both beginners and experienced cattle owners.

Origin and Historical Development of Ayrshire Cattle

The Ayrshire breed traces its roots to the County of Ayr in southwestern Scotland, a region characterized by rugged terrain, variable weather conditions, and relatively modest agricultural resources. It was within this challenging environment that the foundation of the breed was formed during the 18th century. Local cattle were selectively improved through careful crossbreeding with other European dairy types, resulting in an animal that combined hardiness with efficient milk production.

Early farmers in Ayrshire sought cattle that could thrive under less-than-ideal conditions while still producing a dependable supply of milk. Over time, selective breeding emphasized traits such as strong udders, moderate body size, and the ability to convert forage into high-quality milk. By the early 19th century, the breed had stabilized enough to gain recognition, and formal breed standards began to emerge.

The development of Ayrshire cattle reflects a practical and functional approach to animal husbandry. Rather than focusing solely on maximizing output, breeders prioritized balance—ensuring that productivity did not come at the expense of durability or adaptability. This philosophy continues to define the breed today.

Geographic Spread and Global Significance

From its Scottish origins, the Ayrshire breed expanded rapidly beyond the British Isles. By the early 1800s, Ayrshire cattle had been exported to countries such as the United States, Canada, and various parts of Northern Europe. Their reputation for hardiness and consistent milk production made them particularly attractive to farmers operating in climates similar to Scotland's.

In North America, Ayrshires gained popularity for their ability to perform well in colder regions while maintaining good milk quality. Over time, the breed established a strong presence in both small family farms and more structured dairy enterprises. Their adaptability also led to successful introduction in regions with warmer climates, including parts of Africa, Australia, and South America.

Globally, Ayrshire cattle are recognized as a versatile dairy breed capable of performing under a wide range of environmental and management conditions. While they may not always dominate in terms of sheer milk volume compared to some specialized breeds, their consistency, efficiency, and longevity have secured their place in sustainable dairy systems worldwide.

Their global significance lies not only in production but also in their contribution to genetic diversity within the dairy industry. Ayrshires are often valued in breeding programs aimed at improving traits such as fertility, longevity, and structural soundness in dairy herds.

Key Physical and Production Traits

Ayrshire cattle are easily recognizable due to their distinctive appearance and well-balanced conformation. They typically display a combination of red and white coloring, with patterns that vary from deep mahogany to lighter shades. This striking coloration is one of the breed's hallmark features.

In terms of size, Ayrshires are considered medium-framed dairy cattle. This moderate size contributes to their efficiency, as they require fewer resources to maintain compared to larger breeds. Their body structure reflects functionality, with strong legs, well-developed udders, and a frame designed to support sustained milk production.

One of the most notable physical traits of Ayrshire cattle is their udder quality. Well-attached udders with evenly spaced teats are a defining characteristic, contributing to ease of milking and long-term productivity. Their structural soundness also supports longevity, allowing many animals to remain productive for extended periods.

From a production standpoint, Ayrshires are known for producing milk with a favorable balance of butterfat and protein. This makes their milk suitable for a wide range of dairy products, including cheese and butter. Rather than focusing solely on volume, Ayrshires offer a combination of quantity and quality that appeals to both traditional and modern dairy operations.

Their efficient feed-to-milk conversion is another key trait. Ayrshires are capable of maintaining steady production levels without excessive resource demands, making them particularly valuable in systems where efficiency is a priority.

Unique Advantages of the Ayrshire Breed

The Ayrshire breed offers a range of advantages that distinguish it from other dairy cattle. One of the most significant is its adaptability. Developed in a region with challenging environmental conditions, Ayrshires have retained the ability to perform well across diverse climates and terrains.

Durability is another defining advantage. Ayrshires are known for their strong constitution and resistance to many of the stresses associated with dairy production. This resilience contributes to their longevity, allowing farmers to benefit from extended productive lifespans.

Their balanced production profile is also noteworthy. While some breeds may excel in one area at the expense of others, Ayrshires provide a well-rounded performance that includes consistent milk yield, good milk composition, and reliable reproductive efficiency.

Temperament is an additional factor that enhances their appeal. Ayrshires are generally alert and active, with a level of intelligence that can make them responsive to handling. While they may exhibit more energy than some other breeds, this trait can be advantageous in systems that require animals to graze or move regularly.

Another key advantage is their suitability for sustainable and low-input farming systems. Ayrshires are often able to maintain productivity with fewer external inputs, making them a practical choice for farmers seeking to balance profitability with environmental responsibility.

Suitability for Different Farming Systems

Ayrshire cattle are uniquely positioned to perform well in a variety of farming systems, from small-scale operations to larger commercial enterprises. Their adaptability allows them to integrate effectively into both traditional and modern agricultural models.

In smaller or family-run farms, Ayrshires are valued for their manageable size, efficient production, and ability to thrive under less intensive conditions. Their resilience makes them particularly suitable for farmers who may not have access to extensive resources or specialized infrastructure.

In pasture-based systems, Ayrshires excel due to their natural foraging ability and mobility. Their active nature supports grazing-based operations, where animals are expected to utilize available pasture efficiently.

For more structured or commercial dairy systems, Ayrshires offer consistency and reliability. Their balanced production and strong physical traits make them compatible with organized herd management practices, while their longevity contributes to long-term operational stability.

They are also well-suited for mixed farming systems, where dairy production is combined with other agricultural activities. Their versatility allows them to adapt to varying management approaches without significant loss of performance.

Why Ayrshire Cattle Are Ideal for Beginners and Professionals

One of the most compelling aspects of Ayrshire cattle is their ability to meet the needs of both beginners and experienced professionals. For newcomers to cattle ownership, Ayrshires offer a manageable entry point into dairy farming. Their adaptability and efficiency reduce the complexity often associated with livestock management, allowing beginners to build confidence and experience over time.

Their balanced nature means that new owners are less likely to encounter extreme challenges related to maintenance or performance. This makes Ayrshires a practical choice for those seeking to learn and grow within the field.

For experienced farmers, Ayrshires provide opportunities for refinement and optimization. Their consistent performance and strong genetic foundation allow for strategic improvements in herd quality and productivity. Professionals can leverage the breed's strengths to achieve specific goals, whether focused on milk quality, efficiency, or long-term sustainability.

The breed's versatility ensures that it remains relevant across different levels of expertise. Beginners benefit from its forgiving nature, while experts appreciate its potential for advanced management and improvement.

Setting the Foundation for the Handbook

Understanding Ayrshire cattle begins with recognizing the balance that defines the breed. From their origins in Scotland to their global presence today, Ayrshires embody a combination of resilience, efficiency, and adaptability that has stood the test of time.

This handbook is designed to build upon that foundation, guiding readers through every aspect of Ayrshire cattle ownership and management. By starting with a clear understanding of the breed's background and defining characteristics, readers are better prepared to explore the more detailed topics that follow.

Whether your goal is to start a small dairy operation, expand an existing herd, or deepen your knowledge of cattle management, Ayrshire cattle offer a pathway that is both practical and rewarding. Their enduring value lies not only in what they produce, but in how they fit into a wide range of farming systems and approaches.

As you continue through this book, you will gain deeper insights into the principles and practices that support successful Ayrshire cattle management. This introductory chapter serves as the starting point for that journey, providing the context and perspective needed to fully appreciate the potential of this remarkable breed.

Chapter 2

Understanding Breed Standards and Identification

A clear understanding of breed standards and accurate identification is essential for anyone working with Ayrshire cattle. Whether you are a beginner selecting your first animals or a seasoned professional refining herd quality, the ability to recognize true breed characteristics and evaluate individual animals is a foundational skill. Ayrshire cattle are known for their distinct appearance, structural balance, and functional design, all of which contribute to their long-standing reputation as a reliable dairy breed. This chapter provides a detailed and practical guide to identifying Ayrshire cattle, understanding official standards, and evaluating quality with confidence.

Physical Traits of Ayrshire Cattle

Ayrshire cattle are easily distinguished by their striking physical appearance and well-proportioned body structure. Their most recognizable feature is their coat coloration, which consists of a combination of red and white markings. The red can vary significantly in shade, ranging from deep mahogany to lighter reddish-brown tones. The patterning is highly variable—some animals may be predominantly white with red patches, while others may display a more even distribution of color. This variability adds to the visual uniqueness of the breed while still conforming to accepted standards.

In terms of size, Ayrshires are considered a medium-sized dairy breed. Mature cows typically exhibit a balanced frame that is neither excessively large nor overly compact. This moderate size contributes to their efficiency and ease of management. Their body structure reflects functionality, with a strong, straight back, a deep chest, and well-sprung ribs that support internal capacity.

The head of an Ayrshire is clean and well-defined, often displaying a slightly dished profile. The eyes are bright and alert, indicating awareness and vitality. Ears are moderately sized and positioned to complement the head's symmetry. Traditionally, Ayrshires were horned, with horns that curve outward and upward in a graceful shape. However, modern breeding practices have introduced polled (naturally hornless) individuals, which are increasingly common.

Legs and feet are critical components of the breed's physical structure. Ayrshires are known for having strong, well-placed legs that support mobility and durability. The hooves are typically hard and well-formed, contributing to their ability to move efficiently across different terrains.

One of the most important physical traits in Ayrshire cattle is the udder structure. A high-quality Ayrshire udder is well-attached both in the front and rear, forming a strong and balanced support system. The udder should be symmetrical, with evenly spaced teats of moderate size and correct placement. This structure not only contributes to ease of milking but also supports long-term productivity.

Official Breed Standards and Classifications

Breed standards serve as a guideline for what constitutes a true Ayrshire. These standards are established by breed associations and are used to evaluate animals in both commercial and show settings. While specific criteria may vary slightly between regions, the core principles remain consistent.

An ideal Ayrshire cow should demonstrate a combination of dairy strength, structural correctness, and functional efficiency. Dairy strength refers to the balance between angularity and robustness. The animal should appear refined yet strong, with a frame that supports sustained production without excess bulk.

Conformation plays a central role in breed standards. Judges and evaluators look for animals with a level topline, a well-angled rump, and proper alignment of the legs. The overall impression should be one of balance and harmony, where no single feature appears exaggerated or out of proportion.

Udder quality is often given significant emphasis in classification systems. A well-attached udder with strong support and proper teat placement is considered a hallmark of the breed. Evaluators assess not only the appearance of the udder but also its functionality and durability over time.

Classification systems may include scoring or grading animals based on these traits. Categories often range from basic classifications to higher levels of excellence, reflecting the animal's adherence to breed standards. These systems provide a structured way to assess and compare animals, supporting both breeding decisions and herd improvement efforts.

Identifying Purebred vs Crossbred Ayrshires

Distinguishing between purebred and crossbred Ayrshire cattle requires careful observation and attention to detail. Purebred Ayrshires consistently exhibit the defining traits of the breed, including their characteristic coloration, body structure, and overall conformation.

One of the first indicators of a purebred Ayrshire is uniformity in type. While individual variation exists, purebred animals tend to display a consistent set of characteristics that align with breed standards. This includes their medium frame, balanced proportions, and distinctive red-and-white coat patterns.

Crossbred animals may retain some Ayrshire traits but often display characteristics from other breeds. This can result in variations in size, color distribution, or structural features that deviate from the standard. For example, a crossbred animal might exhibit a different body shape, altered udder structure, or coloration that does not align with typical Ayrshire patterns.

Another important factor in identification is pedigree information. Purebred animals are usually accompanied by documented lineage, which confirms their genetic background. While visual assessment is valuable, pedigree records provide an additional layer of certainty.

It is important to note that crossbreeding is not inherently negative. In some cases, crossbred animals may offer desirable traits for specific farming goals. However, for those seeking to maintain breed purity or participate in breed-specific programs, accurate identification is essential.

Behavioral Tendencies and Temperament

Ayrshire cattle are known for their alert and active temperament. They tend to be more energetic than some other dairy breeds, which can be both an advantage and a consideration depending on the management system. Their alertness often translates into responsiveness, making them aware of their surroundings and capable of adapting to different environments.

Despite their energy, Ayrshires are generally manageable and can develop a level of familiarity with handlers over time. Their behavior is influenced by both genetics and environment, and consistent handling can contribute to calmer interactions.

Social behavior is another important aspect of the breed. Ayrshires, like all cattle, are herd animals and exhibit structured social dynamics. They establish hierarchies within the group, which can influence movement and interaction. Understanding these dynamics helps in interpreting behavior and ensuring smooth herd management.

Temperament plays a role in overall evaluation, as animals that are excessively aggressive or overly timid may present challenges. A well-balanced Ayrshire should display alertness without undue nervousness, and confidence without aggression.

How to Evaluate Quality Ayrshire Cattle

Evaluating the quality of Ayrshire cattle involves a combination of visual assessment, structural analysis, and an understanding of breed standards. For beginners, the process may seem complex, but with practice and attention to key traits, it becomes more intuitive.

The first step in evaluation is observing the overall balance of the animal. A high-quality Ayrshire should present a harmonious appearance, where all parts of the body are proportionate and aligned. This includes the relationship between the front and rear, the length of the body, and the placement of the legs.

Structural correctness is a critical factor. The animal should stand squarely, with legs positioned to support weight evenly. The topline should be straight and strong, and the rump should have a slight slope that supports functional movement.

Attention should also be given to dairy character. This refers to the animal's ability to convert resources into milk production, often reflected in traits such as angularity, openness of rib, and overall refinement. A balance between strength and dairy character is ideal.

Udder evaluation is one of the most detailed aspects of quality assessment. A well-structured udder should be firmly attached, symmetrical, and free from defects. Teat placement should allow for efficient milking, and the overall structure should indicate durability.

Movement is another important indicator of quality. Observing an animal as it walks can reveal insights into leg structure and overall soundness. Smooth, confident movement suggests a well-built animal capable of sustained activity.

For expert-level evaluation, attention extends to finer details such as bone quality, skin texture, and the integration of different body parts. Experienced evaluators develop an eye for subtle differences that can influence long-term performance and value.

Bridging Beginner Understanding and Expert Insight

For beginners, learning to identify and evaluate Ayrshire cattle begins with recognizing the most visible traits—color patterns, size, and general structure. As familiarity grows, attention can shift to more detailed aspects such as udder quality, leg placement, and overall balance.

Experts, on the other hand, approach evaluation with a deeper understanding of how individual traits interact. They consider not only how an animal looks but also how its structure supports long-term productivity and durability. This level of insight allows for more precise selection and improvement.

The key is to develop a systematic approach to evaluation. By consistently observing and comparing animals, both beginners and professionals can refine their skills and make informed decisions.

Chapter 3

Planning for Ayrshire Cattle Ownership

Successful Ayrshire cattle ownership begins long before the first animal arrives on your property. Careful planning is the foundation that determines whether your experience will be efficient, profitable, and sustainable—or frustrating and costly. This chapter focuses on the strategic decisions that must be made before acquiring Ayrshire cattle, helping both beginners and experienced farmers align their goals, resources, and expectations.

Ayrshire cattle are known for their adaptability and balanced performance, but like any livestock, they require thoughtful preparation. By clearly defining your purpose, evaluating your available resources, and understanding the broader context of ownership, you position yourself for long-term success.

Defining Ownership Goals

The first and most critical step in planning is defining why you want to keep Ayrshire cattle. Your goals will shape every decision that follows, from land use to financial investment and long-term strategy.

For many owners, dairy production is the primary objective. In this case, your focus will be on consistent milk output, efficiency, and quality. Ayrshires are particularly well-suited for this purpose due to their balanced milk composition and reliable production patterns. However, even within dairy-focused systems, there are variations—some may aim for small-scale household production, while others pursue larger commercial operations.

Another common goal is breeding. Owners who focus on breeding are interested in maintaining or improving genetic quality, often with the intention of selling offspring or contributing to breed development. This approach requires a long-term perspective and a strong understanding of breed standards and selection principles.

Mixed farming represents a more diversified approach. In this system, Ayrshire cattle are integrated into a broader agricultural framework that may include crop production, other livestock, or multiple income streams. This model emphasizes flexibility and resource efficiency, allowing owners to balance different aspects of farm productivity.

It is essential to define your primary goal clearly, but also to recognize that goals can evolve over time. Beginners may start with a simple objective and expand as their experience grows. Professionals may refine their focus to improve efficiency or specialize further. Regardless of your starting point, clarity of purpose is the anchor that guides all planning decisions.

Land Requirements and Space Planning

Land is one of the most important resources in cattle ownership, and its effective use requires careful consideration. Ayrshire cattle, while adaptable, still depend on adequate space to function efficiently and maintain productivity.

The amount of land required depends on several factors, including herd size, management style, and environmental conditions. As a general principle, space should allow for natural movement, grazing opportunities, and separation when needed. Overcrowding can lead to inefficiencies, increased stress, and long-term challenges, while excessive unused land may indicate poor resource utilization.

Space planning is not only about quantity but also about organization. Land should be viewed as a system, where different areas serve specific purposes. This includes designated grazing zones, movement pathways, and areas reserved for operational activities. Even at the planning stage, it is important to think in terms of flow—how animals will move, how tasks will be carried out, and how space will support daily operations.

Topography also plays a role in land suitability. Flat or gently sloping land is generally easier to manage, while steep or uneven terrain may require additional considerations. Soil quality and drainage are equally important, as they influence the usability of the land and its ability to support consistent activity.

For beginners, a common mistake is underestimating the importance of space planning. It is not enough to have land; it must be functional and aligned with your goals. For professionals, the challenge often lies in optimizing existing land to improve efficiency and scalability.

Climate and Environmental Suitability

Ayrshire cattle are known for their resilience and ability to adapt to different climates, but environmental conditions still play a significant role in overall success. Understanding your local climate and how it interacts with your farming system is a critical part of planning.

In regions with cooler temperatures, Ayrshires often perform well due to their origins in Scotland. Their natural hardiness allows them to maintain productivity in less favorable weather conditions. However, this does not mean they are limited to such environments. Ayrshires have also demonstrated adaptability in warmer climates, provided that environmental factors are managed appropriately.

Seasonal variations must be considered. Changes in temperature, rainfall, and daylight can influence how your system operates throughout the year. Planning should account for these fluctuations, ensuring that your approach remains consistent and effective regardless of season.

Environmental factors extend beyond climate to include elements such as water availability, vegetation, and overall ecosystem balance. Access to reliable water sources is essential, while the condition of the land itself influences how effectively it can support cattle.

For beginners, one of the most common mistakes is assuming that a breed's adaptability eliminates the need for environmental planning. While Ayrshires are versatile, aligning your system with local conditions enhances efficiency and reduces potential challenges. For experienced farmers, environmental planning becomes an opportunity to refine and optimize operations, ensuring that resources are used effectively.

Legal and Zoning Considerations

Cattle ownership is not only a practical endeavor but also a regulated activity. Understanding the legal framework in your area is essential to avoid complications and ensure compliance.

Zoning laws determine whether livestock can be kept on a particular property and may impose restrictions on herd size, land use, or operational practices. Before acquiring Ayrshire cattle, it is important to confirm that your property is appropriately zoned for agricultural use.

Permits and registrations may also be required, depending on local regulations. These can include livestock identification systems, land use permits, or participation in agricultural programs. While these requirements may vary, they are an integral part of responsible ownership.

In addition to zoning and permits, there may be guidelines related to environmental impact, waste management, and community considerations. These regulations are designed to ensure that agricultural activities are conducted responsibly and sustainably.

Beginners often overlook the importance of legal preparation, focusing instead on the practical aspects of cattle ownership. However, failing to address regulatory requirements can lead to significant challenges. For professionals, staying informed about evolving regulations is equally important, as compliance supports long-term stability and credibility.

Initial Budgeting Overview

Financial planning is a cornerstone of successful cattle ownership. Before acquiring Ayrshire cattle, it is essential to develop a clear understanding of the costs involved and how they align with your goals.

Initial costs typically include the purchase of animals, land preparation, and essential equipment. However, it is important to view these expenses within the broader context of your operation. Budgeting is not only about what you spend initially but also about how those investments support long-term productivity.

A well-structured budget considers both fixed and variable costs. Fixed costs are those that remain relatively constant, while variable costs may fluctuate based on factors such as herd size or operational scale. Understanding this distinction helps in creating a realistic financial plan.

One of the key aspects of budgeting is anticipating unexpected expenses. Even with careful planning, unforeseen costs can arise, and having a financial buffer provides stability. This is particularly important for beginners, who may encounter challenges as they gain experience.

For professionals, budgeting becomes a tool for optimization. By analyzing costs and returns, experienced farmers can identify areas for improvement and enhance overall efficiency. Financial planning is not a one-time activity but an ongoing process that evolves with your operation.

Avoiding Common Beginner Mistakes

Planning for Ayrshire cattle ownership involves more than understanding individual components—it requires integrating them into a cohesive strategy. Beginners often make the mistake of focusing on one aspect while neglecting others, leading to imbalances that can affect overall success.

One common error is starting without clearly defined goals. Without a clear purpose, decisions become reactive rather than strategic, resulting in inefficiencies and missed opportunities. Another mistake is underestimating resource requirements, particularly in terms of land and finances.

Ignoring environmental and legal considerations is another frequent oversight. These factors may not be immediately visible, but they have a significant impact on long-term operations. Addressing them early prevents complications later.

Finally, impatience can be a challenge. Cattle ownership is a long-term commitment, and rushing into decisions without proper planning can lead to setbacks. Taking the time to prepare thoroughly creates a strong foundation for future growth.

Building a Strong Foundation

Planning for Ayrshire cattle ownership is a process that combines vision, analysis, and preparation. By defining your goals, evaluating your resources, and understanding the broader context of ownership, you create a roadmap that guides your journey.

Ayrshire cattle offer versatility and reliability, but their potential is best realized when supported by thoughtful planning. This chapter serves as a guide to making informed decisions, helping you avoid common pitfalls and approach ownership with confidence.

As you move forward in this handbook, the principles outlined here will continue to shape your understanding and approach. A well-planned foundation not only supports immediate success but also enables long-term growth, ensuring that your experience with Ayrshire cattle is both productive and rewarding.

Chapter 4

Housing and Farm Setup

Designing the right housing and farm setup for Ayrshire cattle is a critical step that directly influences efficiency, safety, and long-term productivity. Unlike many other aspects of cattle management, infrastructure decisions are often long-lasting and costly to change once implemented. Therefore, a well-planned system must balance practicality, durability, and adaptability from the outset.

This chapter provides a structured guide to creating a functional and efficient environment for Ayrshire cattle, covering barn design, pasture organization, shelter considerations, fencing systems, and water access. Whether you are starting from scratch or optimizing an existing setup, the principles outlined here will help you build a system that supports both immediate needs and future growth.

Barn Design and Layout Principles

A well-designed barn serves as the operational center of your cattle system. It is not simply a structure for housing animals, but a space that supports workflow, safety, and efficiency.

At the core of barn design is the principle of functionality. Every element of the layout should serve a clear purpose and contribute to smooth daily operations. This begins with space allocation. Animals should have sufficient room to move comfortably without congestion, while still allowing for efficient use of available space.

Ventilation is one of the most important design considerations. Proper airflow helps regulate temperature, reduces moisture buildup, and maintains a clean environment. Natural ventilation systems, such as open ridges and sidewall openings, are often effective and cost-efficient. Advanced systems may incorporate controlled airflow mechanisms for greater precision.

Lighting also plays a key role. Natural light should be maximized wherever possible, as it supports visibility and creates a more comfortable environment. Artificial lighting should be strategically placed to ensure consistent illumination during early mornings, evenings, or low-light conditions.

The layout flow of the barn is another critical factor. Movement pathways should be clearly defined, allowing animals to enter and exit areas without obstruction. Equipment access points should be positioned to minimize unnecessary movement and reduce labor effort.

For beginners, a simple and straightforward design is often the most effective starting point. Focus on creating a clean, open space with clear pathways and essential features. For advanced operations, optimization may include refining traffic flow, improving space utilization, and integrating systems that enhance efficiency.

Pasture Setup and Rotational Grazing Systems

Pasture is a fundamental component of Ayrshire cattle systems, particularly in operations that emphasize natural grazing. Effective pasture setup is not just about providing land—it is about managing that land as a dynamic resource.

The first step in pasture planning is division. Large areas should be divided into smaller sections, allowing for controlled grazing patterns. This approach supports rotational grazing, where cattle are moved between sections to allow previously grazed areas to recover.

Rotational systems improve land productivity by preventing overuse and encouraging regrowth. They also promote even utilization of pasture, reducing waste and maintaining consistent ground conditions. For beginners, a basic rotation system with a few sections is sufficient to establish the concept. For professionals, more advanced systems may involve multiple divisions and carefully timed rotations.

Access and movement within pasture systems should be planned carefully. Pathways should allow for easy movement between sections without disrupting other areas. Gates and access points should be positioned to support smooth transitions.

Terrain management is another important consideration. Uneven or poorly drained areas can affect usability and should be identified during the planning phase. Adjustments may be needed to ensure that all sections of the pasture contribute effectively to the system.

A common mistake is treating pasture as a static resource. In reality, it requires active management and thoughtful organization. A well-planned pasture system not only supports cattle but also enhances the overall efficiency of the operation.

Shelter and Weather Protection

While Ayrshire cattle are known for their resilience, providing adequate shelter is essential for maintaining comfort and productivity across different weather conditions.

Shelter design should account for both protection and accessibility. Animals should have access to covered areas that shield them from rain, wind, and extreme sunlight. At the same time, these areas should be easy to enter and exit, avoiding congestion or restricted movement.

In colder climates, shelter focuses on reducing exposure to harsh conditions. Windbreaks and enclosed spaces help maintain a stable environment. In warmer climates, the emphasis shifts to shade and airflow, ensuring that animals remain comfortable during high temperatures.

Orientation of shelter structures plays a significant role. Positioning shelters to take advantage of natural wind patterns and sunlight can improve their effectiveness. For example, aligning openings away from prevailing winds can enhance protection, while allowing sunlight to enter during cooler periods.

For beginners, simple shelter solutions such as open-sided structures or natural windbreaks can be highly effective. Advanced setups may incorporate more sophisticated designs that optimize airflow and environmental control.

The key is to provide consistent protection without restricting natural movement or creating unnecessary complexity.

Fencing Systems and Safety

Fencing is one of the most critical components of farm infrastructure, serving both as a boundary and a management tool. A well-designed fencing system ensures safety, supports organization, and facilitates efficient movement.

The primary purpose of fencing is containment. It must be strong enough to prevent animals from escaping while remaining durable over time. Materials and construction methods should be selected based on the specific needs of the operation.

Visibility is an often-overlooked aspect of fencing. Clearly visible boundaries help animals recognize limits and reduce the likelihood of accidental contact. This contributes to both safety and ease of management.

Division fencing within the farm is equally important. Separating different areas allows for better control of movement and supports systems such as rotational grazing. Internal fencing does not always need to be as robust as perimeter fencing but should still be reliable.

Safety considerations extend beyond containment. Fences should be free from sharp edges or weak points that could cause injury. Regular inspection is essential to identify and address potential issues before they become problems.

For beginners, investing in a simple, durable fencing system is a practical starting point. For advanced operations, fencing can be optimized to support more complex management systems, including precise control of movement and efficient use of space.

Water Access Systems

Access to water is a fundamental requirement for Ayrshire cattle, and the way it is provided can significantly influence efficiency and overall system performance.

A well-designed water system ensures that animals have consistent and convenient access at all times. Water points should be strategically located to minimize travel distance and prevent crowding. In pasture systems, this may involve placing water sources within or near each grazing section.

Reliability is a key factor. Water systems should be designed to function consistently under different conditions, including changes in weather or usage levels. Backup options or redundancy can provide additional security, particularly in larger operations.

The distribution system should support even access. If water points are too limited or poorly positioned, it can lead to competition and uneven usage patterns. Proper placement helps maintain balance and reduces stress within the herd.

For beginners, simple water setups such as troughs connected to a reliable source can be effective. For advanced systems, more sophisticated distribution networks may be used to ensure efficiency across larger areas.

Maintenance is also an important consideration. Water systems should be easy to monitor and maintain, ensuring that they remain clean and functional over time.

Integrating the System for Efficiency

While each component—barns, pasture, shelter, fencing, and water—serves a specific purpose, the true strength of a farm setup lies in how these elements work together as a unified system.

Integration begins with flow and connectivity. Movement between different areas should be smooth and logical, reducing unnecessary effort and improving efficiency. For example, pathways should connect barns to pasture areas in a way that supports natural movement patterns.

Scalability is another important factor. A well-designed system should allow for expansion or modification without requiring a complete overhaul. This is particularly important for beginners who may start small and grow over time.

Flexibility also plays a role. Conditions can change, and the ability to adapt your setup ensures long-term sustainability.

Designing with flexibility in mind allows you to respond to new challenges or opportunities.

Chapter 5

Equipment and Essential Farm Tools

Efficient Ayrshire cattle management depends not only on knowledge and planning but also on the quality and suitability of equipment used on the farm. The right tools reduce labor, improve consistency, enhance safety, and support long-term productivity. Whether you are a beginner establishing a small setup or a professional managing a large operation, selecting and organizing equipment correctly is a critical step toward operational success.

This chapter provides a comprehensive guide to the essential equipment required for Ayrshire cattle systems, including milking systems, feeding and watering tools, cleaning equipment, handling tools, and maintenance practices. Each category is approached with both simplicity and scalability in mind, ensuring that readers at all levels can build or refine their systems effectively.

Milking Equipment Types and Systems

Milking equipment represents one of the most important investments in any dairy-focused operation. The type of system you choose should align with your scale, workflow, and long-term goals.

For beginners or small-scale setups, manual or portable milking systems are often the starting point. These systems are relatively simple, cost-effective, and easy to operate. Portable milking machines typically consist of a vacuum unit, milking cluster, and collection container. They allow for flexibility and can be used in different areas of the farm without requiring permanent installation.

As operations grow, pipeline milking systems become more practical. These systems use fixed lines to transport milk from the milking point to a central collection area. They improve efficiency by reducing manual handling and allowing for more streamlined operations. Pipeline systems are particularly beneficial for farms with multiple animals, as they support consistent and organized milking routines.

At a more advanced level, milking parlors represent a highly efficient solution for larger herds. These setups are designed to optimize flow, allowing animals to be milked in a structured and controlled environment. Parlors can vary in design, including herringbone, parallel, and rotary configurations, each offering specific advantages depending on herd size and management preferences.

Automation is increasingly becoming a feature of modern milking systems. Advanced setups may include automated units that monitor output, track performance, and reduce manual labor. While these systems require significant investment, they offer long-term benefits in efficiency and data-driven management.

Regardless of the system chosen, the key considerations are reliability, ease of use, and compatibility with your overall farm layout. Equipment should integrate smoothly into your workflow, minimizing disruptions and supporting consistent performance.

Feeding and Watering Tools

Feeding and watering tools play a central role in maintaining an organized and efficient system. While feeding strategies are addressed separately, the tools used to deliver and manage resources are essential components of daily operations.

Basic feeding tools include feed troughs, bins, and storage containers. These should be durable, easy to clean, and designed to minimize waste. For smaller setups, simple troughs placed in accessible locations are sufficient. For larger operations, more structured systems such as feed bunks or automated feeders may be used to improve efficiency.

Feed storage solutions are equally important. Proper storage protects feed from contamination, moisture, and spoilage. Containers or silos should be designed to maintain quality while allowing easy access for distribution.

Watering tools must ensure consistent and reliable access. Water troughs are the most common solution, available in various sizes and materials. They should be positioned to allow easy access while preventing overcrowding. Automatic waterers are a more advanced option, providing a continuous supply without the need for manual refilling.

The placement of feeding and watering tools should support natural movement and reduce competition. Strategic positioning improves accessibility and contributes to a smoother workflow.

For beginners, simplicity and durability are the priorities. For professionals, the focus shifts to efficiency, scalability, and integration with broader systems.

Cleaning and Sanitation Tools

Maintaining a clean environment is essential for operational efficiency and long-term sustainability. Cleaning and sanitation tools support this goal by ensuring that equipment and facilities remain in good condition.

Basic cleaning tools include brushes, scrapers, and shovels, which are used to remove debris and maintain cleanliness in various areas. These tools should be sturdy and easy to handle, allowing for regular use without excessive effort.

Pressure washers are a valuable addition to any farm setup. They provide a quick and effective way to clean surfaces, equipment, and areas that require thorough sanitation. For larger operations, high-capacity washers can significantly reduce cleaning time.

Sanitation also involves the use of disinfectants and cleaning solutions. These products help maintain hygiene standards and prevent contamination. Storage and handling of these materials should be organized to ensure safe and efficient use.

For advanced systems, automated cleaning equipment may be incorporated. These systems are designed to handle routine cleaning tasks with minimal manual intervention, improving consistency and reducing labor requirements.

The key to effective sanitation is consistency. Tools should be readily accessible and maintained in good condition, allowing for regular and thorough cleaning without disruption to daily operations.

Handling and Restraint Equipment

Safe and effective handling of Ayrshire cattle requires the use of appropriate equipment. Handling tools are designed to guide movement, reduce stress, and ensure safety for both animals and handlers.

Basic equipment includes gates, panels, and chutes, which are used to control movement and create defined pathways. These structures should be strong, secure, and easy to adjust, allowing for flexibility in different situations.

Head gates and restraint systems provide a controlled way to secure animals when necessary. These tools are designed to hold the animal safely without causing harm, enabling tasks to be carried out efficiently.

Portable handling equipment is particularly useful for smaller operations or setups that require flexibility. Panels and temporary enclosures can be arranged as needed, providing adaptable solutions for different scenarios.

For larger or more advanced systems, integrated handling facilities may be used. These setups are designed to streamline movement and improve efficiency, often incorporating multiple components into a cohesive system.

Safety is the primary consideration when selecting handling equipment. All tools should be free from sharp edges, properly secured, and designed to minimize risk. Regular inspection ensures that equipment remains reliable and effective.

Equipment Maintenance Systems

Even the best equipment requires proper maintenance to remain effective over time. A structured maintenance system ensures that tools and machinery continue to perform as expected, reducing downtime and extending their lifespan.

The foundation of maintenance is regular inspection. Equipment should be checked for signs of wear, damage, or malfunction. Identifying issues early allows for timely repairs and prevents larger problems.

Cleaning and storage are also critical aspects of maintenance. Tools should be cleaned after use and stored in a designated area to protect them from damage and environmental exposure. Organized storage systems make it easier to locate and manage equipment.

Lubrication and servicing are necessary for mechanical components. Moving parts should be maintained according to manufacturer guidelines, ensuring smooth operation and preventing unnecessary wear.

For advanced operations, maintenance may include scheduled servicing programs and record-keeping systems. Tracking maintenance activities helps ensure consistency and provides valuable insights into equipment performance.

A common mistake is neglecting maintenance until problems arise. Proactive care not only preserves equipment but also supports overall efficiency and reliability.

Balancing Beginner Essentials and Professional Upgrades

The selection of equipment should always align with your current needs while allowing room for future growth. Beginners should focus on acquiring essential tools that are reliable, easy to use, and cost-effective. Starting with a simple setup provides a solid foundation and allows for gradual expansion.

As operations grow, upgrading equipment becomes a strategic decision. Professional systems are designed to improve efficiency, reduce labor, and support larger-scale management. These upgrades should be implemented thoughtfully, ensuring that they integrate seamlessly with existing infrastructure.

It is important to avoid overinvestment at the early stages. Acquiring advanced equipment without the capacity to utilize it effectively can lead to inefficiencies. Instead, build your system progressively, adding tools and upgrades as your needs evolve.

Chapter 6

Nutrition and Feeding Management

Nutrition is one of the most influential factors in the performance, productivity, and overall efficiency of Ayrshire cattle. A well-structured feeding system supports growth, milk production, body condition, and long-term sustainability. Unlike infrastructure or equipment, nutrition is a dynamic element—constantly adapting to life stages, environmental conditions, and operational goals.

This chapter provides a comprehensive and practical understanding of feeding and nutrition for Ayrshire cattle. It bridges scientific principles with real-world application, ensuring that both beginners and experienced cattle owners can develop effective feeding systems without unnecessary complexity or inefficiency.

Nutritional Requirements by Life Stage

Ayrshire cattle have different nutritional needs depending on their stage of development. Understanding these variations is essential for maintaining balance and ensuring that each animal performs at its best.

In early life, young animals require nutrition that supports rapid growth and development. At this stage, the focus is on building a strong foundation—supporting muscle development, skeletal growth, and overall vitality. Nutritional intake must be sufficient in energy, protein, and essential nutrients to sustain this growth without overburdening the system.

As cattle transition into adolescence, their nutritional requirements shift toward steady development and structural refinement. Growth continues, but at a more controlled pace. Balanced intake becomes critical, ensuring that animals develop evenly without excessive weight gain or deficiencies.

Mature animals require nutrition that supports maintenance and productivity. At this stage, the goal is to sustain body condition while enabling consistent output. Nutritional balance must account for energy demands, metabolic efficiency, and overall stability.

For working or productive animals, nutrient demands increase to support performance. This requires careful adjustment of intake to maintain equilibrium between input and output.

For beginners, a key principle is recognizing that feeding is not static. Each life stage requires thoughtful adjustment. For professionals, the focus shifts to precision—fine-tuning intake to optimize performance while maintaining efficiency.

Forage vs. Concentrate Feeding

The foundation of Ayrshire cattle nutrition lies in the balance between forage and concentrates. Understanding how these two components interact is essential for building an effective feeding system.

Forage refers to fibrous plant material such as grasses and preserved roughage. It forms the natural base of a cattle diet and supports digestive function. Ayrshire cattle, known for their efficiency, perform well on forage-based systems, making this a cornerstone of their feeding strategy.

Forage provides bulk and supports rumen activity, which is critical for nutrient absorption. High-quality forage contributes significantly to overall performance, making its selection and management a priority.

Concentrates, on the other hand, are more energy-dense feeds designed to supplement forage. They provide additional nutrients that may not be available in sufficient quantities from forage alone. Concentrates are particularly useful in supporting higher levels of productivity or compensating for variations in forage quality.

The key is achieving the right balance. Too much reliance on concentrates can reduce efficiency and increase costs, while insufficient supplementation may limit performance. Ayrshire cattle are particularly valued for their ability to maintain productivity with a strong forage base, making them well-suited to systems that emphasize natural feeding.

Beginners should focus on establishing a solid forage foundation, using concentrates as a supportive element rather than a primary source. Advanced systems often involve precise adjustments to this balance, optimizing intake based on performance goals and resource availability.

Pasture-Based Feeding Systems

Pasture-based feeding systems represent one of the most efficient and sustainable approaches to Ayrshire cattle nutrition. These systems utilize natural grazing as the primary source of intake, aligning with the breed's strengths and natural behavior.

A well-managed pasture system allows cattle to harvest their own feed, reducing labor and operational costs. Ayrshires, with their active nature and adaptability, are particularly effective in such environments.

The success of pasture-based systems depends on management and organization. Grazing areas should be structured to allow for controlled use, ensuring that pasture remains productive over time. Rotational grazing is a key strategy, where cattle are moved between sections to allow regrowth and maintain quality.

Pasture quality is a critical factor. Not all grazing areas provide the same nutritional value, and variability must be accounted for. Observing pasture condition and adjusting usage accordingly helps maintain consistency.

Access and distribution also influence effectiveness. Cattle should be able to move freely within designated areas, with minimal disruption. Efficient pathways and well-positioned access points contribute to smooth operation.

For beginners, pasture-based systems offer a natural and cost-effective starting point. For professionals, advanced pasture management techniques can significantly enhance productivity and sustainability.

Seasonal Feeding Strategies

Feeding strategies must adapt to seasonal changes, as environmental conditions directly affect both resource availability and nutritional requirements.

During periods of abundance, such as favorable growing seasons, pasture can provide a substantial portion of nutritional needs. The focus during these times is on maximizing utilization while maintaining pasture health.

In less favorable seasons, when natural resources are limited, adjustments are necessary to ensure consistency. Stored feed and supplemental resources become more important, providing stability when pasture conditions decline.

Temperature variations also influence feeding strategies. In cooler conditions, energy requirements may increase to support body maintenance. In warmer conditions, intake patterns may shift, requiring adjustments to ensure adequate consumption.

Seasonal transitions are particularly important. Sudden changes in diet or environment can disrupt balance, so adjustments should be gradual and well-planned.

Beginners often overlook the impact of seasonal variation, leading to inconsistencies in feeding. Professionals, on the other hand, anticipate these changes and plan accordingly, ensuring that nutrition remains stable throughout the year.

Mineral and Water Requirements

In addition to primary feed components, minerals and water are essential elements of Ayrshire cattle nutrition. These components support a wide range of physiological functions and must be consistently available.

Minerals play a role in structural development, metabolic processes, and overall performance. They are typically provided in the form of supplements that complement the primary diet.

Ensuring access to essential minerals helps maintain balance and supports long-term productivity.

Water is perhaps the most critical component of all. It is involved in digestion, nutrient transport, and temperature regulation. Consistent access to clean water is essential for maintaining intake and supporting overall function.

The availability and quality of water directly influence feeding efficiency. Insufficient or inconsistent access can disrupt intake patterns and reduce performance. Placement of water sources should be strategic, ensuring that all animals can access water بسهولة and without competition.

For beginners, ensuring constant access to clean water and basic mineral supplementation is a fundamental priority. For advanced systems, monitoring and optimizing these components can further enhance efficiency and performance.

Balancing Basic and Advanced Feeding Systems

Effective nutrition management involves balancing simplicity with precision. Beginners should focus on establishing a system that is easy to manage, reliable, and aligned with the natural strengths of Ayrshire cattle. This typically involves a strong forage base, consistent access to water, and basic supplementation.

As experience grows, feeding systems can be refined to improve efficiency and performance. Advanced approaches may involve adjusting intake based on production levels, monitoring body condition, and optimizing resource use.

The goal is not complexity for its own sake, but rather controlled efficiency. Each adjustment should serve a clear purpose, contributing to overall system performance without introducing unnecessary complications.

Chapter 7

Dairy Production and Milk Management

Dairy production is the core strength of Ayrshire cattle, and understanding how to manage milk output effectively is essential for achieving consistent results. Ayrshires are widely respected for their balance of milk quantity and quality, making them a reliable choice for both small-scale and commercial dairy operations. However, maximizing their potential requires a combination of structured routines, proper handling, and attention to factors that influence production.

This chapter focuses on the practical aspects of dairy production and milk management, providing a performance-driven guide for both beginners and experienced operators. By establishing efficient systems and maintaining high standards, you can ensure that milk production remains consistent, profitable, and sustainable.

Milk Production Capacity of Ayrshires

Ayrshire cattle are known for their moderate-to-high milk production capacity, combined with excellent milk composition. Rather than focusing solely on volume, the breed offers a balanced output that includes desirable levels of butterfat and protein. This makes Ayrshire milk particularly valuable for a wide range of dairy applications.

One of the defining characteristics of Ayrshire production is consistency. While some breeds may produce higher peak volumes, Ayrshires often maintain stable output over extended periods. This reliability is especially beneficial for operations that prioritize steady supply rather than short-term peaks.

Another important aspect is efficiency. Ayrshires are capable of converting available resources into milk effectively, making them well-suited for systems that emphasize cost control and sustainability. Their moderate body size contributes to this efficiency, as maintenance requirements are generally lower compared to larger breeds.

Production levels can vary depending on individual animals, environmental conditions, and management systems. However, the breed's strength lies in its ability to deliver dependable performance across different setups.

For beginners, this means a more manageable entry into dairy production, with fewer extremes to navigate. For professionals, it provides a stable foundation that can be optimized for improved results.

Milking Routines and Efficiency

Establishing a consistent and efficient milking routine is essential for maintaining productivity. Routine creates stability, and stability supports performance.

At its core, an effective milking routine is built on consistency in timing and approach. Animals respond well to predictable schedules, and maintaining regular intervals helps support steady production. Variations in timing can disrupt patterns and reduce efficiency.

Efficiency is also influenced by workflow organization. The sequence of actions, movement of animals, and positioning of equipment should all contribute to a smooth and uninterrupted process. Reducing unnecessary steps or delays improves both speed and consistency.

For beginners, simple routines are often the most effective. A clear and repeatable process minimizes confusion and ensures that tasks are completed correctly. As experience grows, routines can be refined to improve efficiency and reduce labor.

In more advanced systems, optimization becomes a key focus. This may involve improving movement flow, reducing handling time, and integrating systems that support faster and more consistent operation. The goal is to achieve a balance between speed and accuracy, ensuring that efficiency does not compromise quality.

Another important factor is environmental calmness. A quiet and controlled environment during milking supports smoother operations and reduces disruptions. Consistency in handling and surroundings contributes to overall efficiency.

Milk Hygiene and Quality Control

Maintaining high standards of hygiene is essential for ensuring milk quality. Cleanliness affects not only the safety of the product but also its value and usability.

The foundation of milk hygiene is clean equipment and clean handling practices. All equipment that comes into contact with milk must be properly cleaned and maintained. Residue or contamination can compromise quality and lead to significant losses.

Environmental cleanliness also plays a role. The area where milking takes place should be kept clean and organized, reducing the risk of contamination. Attention to detail in maintaining a hygienic environment contributes to consistent quality.

Quality control involves monitoring and maintaining standards throughout the process. This includes observing the appearance, consistency, and overall condition of the milk. Any irregularities should be identified and addressed promptly.

For beginners, focusing on basic cleanliness and careful handling is the most important step. Establishing good habits early creates a strong foundation for future improvement.

For professionals, quality control becomes more detailed and systematic. Advanced systems may include regular testing, record-keeping, and continuous monitoring to ensure that standards are consistently met.

Storage and Handling

Proper storage and handling are critical for preserving milk quality after it has been collected. Even high-quality milk can deteriorate quickly if not managed correctly.

The primary goal of storage is to maintain freshness and prevent contamination. This requires appropriate containers and conditions that support stability. Storage systems should be designed to protect the milk from environmental factors such as heat, light, and exposure.

Temperature control is one of the most important aspects of storage. Maintaining a stable and appropriate temperature helps preserve quality and extend usability. Sudden changes or inconsistent conditions can negatively affect the product.

Handling practices should focus on minimizing disruption and exposure. Each transfer or movement introduces the potential for contamination, so processes should be streamlined and controlled.

For beginners, simple storage solutions that prioritize cleanliness and consistency are sufficient. As operations grow, more advanced systems can be introduced to improve efficiency and capacity.

Professional setups often include integrated storage systems that allow for larger volumes and more precise control. These systems are designed to handle increased demand while maintaining high standards of quality.

Factors Affecting Milk Yield

Milk production is influenced by a variety of factors, many of which are interconnected. Understanding these factors allows for better management and more consistent results.

One of the most significant factors is consistency in routine. Irregular schedules or disruptions can affect production levels, making stability a key priority.

Environmental conditions also play a role. Temperature, humidity, and overall comfort can influence output. Providing a stable and supportive environment helps maintain consistent production.

Individual variation is another important consideration. Not all animals will produce at the same level, and recognizing these differences allows for more effective management. Monitoring performance helps identify patterns and areas for improvement.

Resource availability and quality influence production as well. The quality of inputs and the overall management system contribute to how effectively animals can perform.

Stress and handling practices can impact yield. Calm and consistent handling supports better performance, while disruptions or discomfort can reduce output.

For beginners, focusing on stability and consistency is the most effective approach. Avoiding major fluctuations and maintaining a steady system helps support reliable production.

For professionals, optimization involves fine-tuning these factors to achieve higher efficiency. This may include analyzing performance data, adjusting systems, and implementing improvements that enhance output.

Balancing Beginner Systems and Professional Optimization

Dairy production systems should evolve with experience and scale. Beginners benefit from simplicity and clarity, focusing on establishing consistent routines and maintaining basic quality standards. Starting with a manageable system allows for learning and gradual improvement.

As operations grow, the focus shifts to optimization and efficiency. Professional systems are designed to handle larger volumes, reduce labor, and maintain high standards across all aspects of production. This often involves integrating equipment, refining workflows, and implementing monitoring systems.

The transition from basic to advanced systems should be gradual and purposeful. Each upgrade should address a specific need, contributing to overall improvement without introducing unnecessary complexity.

Chapter 8

Health Monitoring and Preventative Care

Maintaining the health of Ayrshire cattle is not primarily about reacting to problems—it is about preventing them before they arise. Preventative care is the foundation of a successful cattle operation, reducing losses, improving productivity, and ensuring long-term sustainability. Ayrshires are known for their resilience, but even the hardiest breed requires consistent monitoring and proactive management to perform at its best.

This chapter focuses on practical, preventative strategies that help you maintain a healthy herd. By developing strong observation habits, implementing structured health protocols, and maintaining a clean and controlled environment, both beginners and professionals can significantly reducc risks and improve overall herd performance.

Daily Health Observation Techniques

The most powerful tool in preventative care is daily observation. Early detection of subtle changes can prevent minor issues from becoming major problems.

Effective observation begins with routine consistency. Checking your cattle at the same time each day allows you to notice deviations from normal behavior. Over time, you develop a mental baseline of what is typical for your herd.

Key areas to observe include:

- Behavior and activity levels: Healthy Ayrshire cattle are generally alert and responsive. A noticeable decrease in activity, isolation from the group, or unusual stillness can indicate a developing issue.
- Posture and movement: Watch how animals stand and walk. Smooth, balanced movement is a sign of

soundness, while stiffness or hesitation may signal discomfort.

- Appetite and intake patterns: While feeding specifics are not discussed here, a general awareness of whether animals are engaging normally with available resources is important. A sudden lack of interest is often an early warning sign.

- Body condition and appearance: Changes in body condition, coat quality, or overall appearance can reflect underlying concerns. A healthy animal typically has a clean, well-maintained coat and a stable body profile.

- Eyes and facial expression: Bright, clear eyes indicate alertness, while dull or sunken eyes may suggest stress or imbalance.

Observation should be both systematic and intuitive. Beginners should use a checklist approach, consciously reviewing each factor. Experienced handlers often rely on instinct developed through repetition, quickly identifying when something feels "off."

A common mistake is rushing through checks or only observing from a distance. Close, attentive observation is essential for accurate assessment.

Vaccination Principles

Vaccination is a key component of preventative health management, designed to prepare the animal's immune system against potential threats. While specific vaccination schedules may vary depending on location and veterinary guidance, understanding the principles behind vaccination is essential.

The primary goal of vaccination is protection through preparedness. By introducing controlled exposure to specific agents, the immune system develops the ability to respond effectively if exposed in the future.

Vaccination programs should be planned and consistent. Irregular or incomplete programs reduce effectiveness and leave gaps in protection. It is important to follow a structured approach that aligns with local conditions and risk factors.

Another key principle is timing. Vaccines are most effective when administered at appropriate stages, ensuring that the immune system responds optimally. Consistency in timing supports long-term effectiveness.

Handling and storage are also critical. Vaccines must be stored under proper conditions and handled carefully to maintain their effectiveness. Improper handling can compromise results.

For beginners, the most important step is establishing a basic vaccination plan in consultation with reliable guidance. For professionals, vaccination programs are often refined to address specific risks and optimize herd-wide protection.

Parasite Control Strategies

Parasites are a common challenge in cattle systems, but with effective preventative strategies, their impact can be minimized. The goal of parasite control is not necessarily complete elimination, but management and reduction to safe levels.

Parasite control begins with awareness of risk factors. Environmental conditions, stocking density, and pasture use all influence parasite presence. Understanding these factors allows for more targeted management.

A key strategy is rotation and spacing. Moving animals between areas and avoiding overuse of specific zones helps reduce parasite buildup. This approach aligns with broader land management practices and contributes to overall system health.

Monitoring is equally important. Observing animals for signs of irritation, discomfort, or changes in condition can provide early indicators of parasite issues. Regular assessment helps ensure that control measures remain effective.

Preventative treatments may be used as part of a structured program. These should be applied strategically rather than excessively, ensuring effectiveness while avoiding unnecessary use.

For beginners, focusing on basic rotation and observation provides a strong starting point. For advanced operations, parasite control becomes more precise, incorporating monitoring data and targeted interventions.

Hoof Care and Grooming

Hoof health is a critical aspect of overall well-being, directly affecting movement, comfort, and productivity. Preventative hoof care ensures that cattle remain mobile and free from unnecessary stress.

Regular visual inspection of hooves is essential. Look for signs of uneven wear, cracks, or abnormalities. Early detection allows for timely correction before issues worsen.

Routine trimming is an important part of hoof maintenance. Properly maintained hooves support balanced movement and reduce strain on joints and muscles. The frequency of trimming depends on conditions and wear patterns, but consistency is key.

The environment also plays a role in hoof health. Clean, dry surfaces help prevent excessive wear and reduce the risk of complications. Attention to ground conditions contributes to long-term hoof stability.

Grooming extends beyond hooves to include coat and general cleanliness. Regular grooming helps maintain skin health, improves appearance, and allows for closer inspection of the animal's condition.

For beginners, simple inspection and periodic maintenance are sufficient to establish good practices. Professionals often implement structured hoof care programs, ensuring consistency across the herd.

Biosecurity Practices

Biosecurity is the practice of protecting your herd from external risks. It involves controlling the introduction and spread of potential threats, ensuring that your system remains stable and secure.

The first principle of biosecurity is controlled access. Limiting who and what enters your farm reduces the risk of introducing unwanted elements. Visitors, equipment, and new animals should all be managed carefully.

Quarantine procedures are a key component. New animals should be kept separate for a period of observation before being introduced to the main herd. This allows time to identify any potential issues without affecting the entire group.

Cleanliness is another important factor. Equipment and tools should be cleaned regularly, especially when used across different areas. This reduces the risk of transferring contaminants.

Movement control within the farm also supports biosecurity. Organized pathways and designated areas help prevent unnecessary mixing and reduce exposure.

For beginners, basic biosecurity measures such as controlled access and cleanliness provide strong protection. For advanced operations, biosecurity becomes more structured, with detailed protocols and monitoring systems.

Building a Preventative Care System

Preventative care is most effective when it is integrated into a consistent and structured system. Each element—observation, vaccination, parasite control, hoof care, and biosecurity—works together to create a comprehensive approach.

The key is consistency. Irregular application of preventative measures reduces their effectiveness. Establishing routines and maintaining them over time ensures that your system remains reliable.

Documentation can also enhance effectiveness. Keeping records of observations, vaccinations, and maintenance activities provides valuable insights and supports decision-making.

For beginners, the focus should be on building simple, repeatable routines. As experience grows, these routines can be expanded and refined to improve efficiency and precision.

Avoiding Common Preventative Care Mistakes

Several common mistakes can undermine preventative efforts:

- Inconsistent observation: Skipping daily checks or performing them superficially can lead to missed early signs.

- Irregular programs: Incomplete vaccination or parasite control reduces effectiveness.

- Neglecting environment: Ignoring cleanliness and conditions can create unnecessary risks.

- Delayed action: Waiting too long to address small issues can lead to larger problems.

Avoiding these mistakes requires discipline and attention to detail. Preventative care is not a one-time effort but an ongoing commitment.

Chapter 9

Common Diseases and Health Challenges

Even in well-managed Ayrshire cattle systems, health challenges can arise. Understanding the most common diseases and disorders is essential for recognizing problems early and responding appropriately. This chapter focuses on the diagnostic and informational aspects of key health issues, helping both beginners and experienced cattle owners identify symptoms, understand causes, and interpret warning signs.

Ayrshire cattle are generally known for their durability and resilience, but like all dairy breeds, they are susceptible to certain conditions related to production demands, environment, and physiological stress. The ability to recognize these challenges quickly can significantly reduce their impact.

Mastitis and Udder Health Issues

Mastitis is one of the most significant health challenges in dairy cattle, directly affecting milk quality and overall productivity. It is an inflammation of the udder tissue, typically caused by bacterial infection.

Symptoms of Mastitis

- Swelling or hardness in the udder
- Heat or sensitivity in affected areas
- Changes in milk appearance (clots, discoloration, watery texture)
- Reduced milk output

- General discomfort or restlessness

In some cases, mastitis may be subclinical, meaning there are no obvious visible signs, but milk quality and production are still affected.

Causes of Mastitis

Mastitis is usually linked to bacterial entry through the teat canal. Contributing factors include:

- Contaminated environments
- Poor udder hygiene
- Physical injury to the udder
- Stress or weakened immunity

The structure of the udder also plays a role. Animals with poorly supported udders or improper teat placement may be more susceptible due to increased exposure.

Understanding the Impact

Mastitis affects both milk quality and economic value. It can lead to reduced production, discarded milk, and long-term udder damage if not addressed. Recognizing early signs is critical for minimizing its effects.

Digestive Disorders

Digestive health is central to the performance of Ayrshire cattle. The complexity of the ruminant digestive system makes it highly efficient, but also vulnerable to imbalances.

Common Digestive Disorders

Bloat

Bloat occurs when gas accumulates in the rumen and cannot be expelled.

Symptoms:

- Swollen left side of the abdomen
- Discomfort or restlessness
- Reduced movement
- Difficulty breathing in severe cases

Causes:

- Rapid fermentation of certain feeds
- Imbalance in rumen function
- Sudden dietary changes

Acidosis

Acidosis results from excessive acid buildup in the rumen.

Symptoms:

- Reduced appetite
- Lethargy
- Loose manure
- Decreased production

Causes:

- High intake of rapidly fermentable feed
- Disruption of rumen balance

Indigestion

Indigestion refers to general disruption of normal digestive processes.

Symptoms:

- Reduced intake
- Irregular rumination
- Changes in manure consistency

Causes:

- Sudden changes in diet
- Stress or environmental shifts

Understanding Digestive Challenges

Digestive disorders often stem from imbalances in the rumen environment. The rumen relies on a stable internal ecosystem, and disruptions can quickly lead to noticeable symptoms. Early recognition is essential to prevent escalation.

Metabolic Diseases

Metabolic diseases are associated with imbalances in the body's internal processes, often linked to energy and nutrient utilization. These conditions are particularly relevant in high-performing dairy animals.

Common Metabolic Conditions

Ketosis

Ketosis occurs when the body relies excessively on fat reserves for energy.

Symptoms:

- Reduced appetite

- Weight loss
- Decreased milk production
- Lethargy

Causes:

- Energy imbalance
- High production demands exceeding intake

Milk Fever (Hypocalcemia)

Milk fever is related to low calcium levels in the blood.

Symptoms:

- Weakness or inability to stand

- Muscle tremors
- Reduced alertness

Causes:

- Sudden calcium demand associated with milk production

Fatty Liver Syndrome

This condition involves excessive fat accumulation in the liver.

Symptoms:

- Reduced appetite
- Decreased production
- General weakness

Causes:

- Prolonged energy imbalance
- Mobilization of fat reserves

Understanding Metabolic Disorders

Metabolic diseases are often linked to physiological stress and imbalance. They may develop gradually, with subtle early signs that can be easily overlooked. Recognizing these signs allows for timely intervention and reduces long-term impact.

Reproductive Health Issues

Reproductive health is a key component of herd sustainability. While Ayrshire cattle are generally reliable in this area, certain challenges can arise.

Common Reproductive Issues

Infertility

Infertility refers to difficulty in achieving successful conception.

Symptoms:

- Repeated unsuccessful breeding attempts
- Irregular reproductive cycles

Causes:

- Hormonal imbalances
- Nutritional deficiencies
- Stress

Retained Placenta

This condition occurs when the placenta is not expelled after birth.

Symptoms:

- Visible retention of placental tissue
- Discomfort or reduced activity

Causes:

- Physiological stress
- Nutritional imbalance
- Complications during calving

Difficult Calving (Dystocia)

Dystocia involves complications during the birthing process.

Symptoms:

- Prolonged labor
- Signs of distress

Causes:

- Size mismatch between calf and dam
- Positioning issues
- Weak contractions

Understanding Reproductive Challenges

Reproductive issues often reflect underlying imbalances or stress factors. They can affect herd productivity and long-term planning. Early recognition of irregular patterns is essential for maintaining reproductive efficiency.

Environmental-Related Illnesses

Environmental conditions play a significant role in cattle health. Changes in temperature, moisture, and overall surroundings can lead to various health challenges.

Common Environmental Issues

Heat Stress

Heat stress occurs when animals are unable to regulate body temperature effectively.

Symptoms:

- Increased respiration rate

- Reduced activity
- Decreased production

Causes:

- High temperatures
- Poor airflow
- Lack of shade

Cold Stress

Cold stress affects animals exposed to low temperatures without adequate protection.

Symptoms:

- Shivering
- Reduced movement
- Increased energy demand

Causes:

- Prolonged exposure to cold
- Wet or windy conditions

Respiratory Issues

Respiratory problems can arise from poor air quality.

Symptoms:

- Coughing

- Nasal discharge
- Labored breathing

Causes:

- Dust
- Poor ventilation
- Accumulation of gases

Understanding Environmental Impact

Environmental illnesses are often preventable through proper conditions, but when they occur, they can significantly affect performance. Recognizing how the environment influences health is key to identifying these issues early.

Recognizing Patterns and Early Warning Signs

While each condition has specific symptoms, there are general warning signs that indicate potential health challenges:

- Sudden changes in behavior
- Decrease in production
- Altered physical appearance
- Reduced interaction with the herd

Recognizing patterns is an essential skill. Changes that may seem minor can often be the first indication of a larger issue.

Diagnostic Awareness for Beginners and Experts

For beginners, the focus should be on recognizing obvious symptoms and understanding basic causes. Building familiarity with normal behavior and appearance is the first step toward effective diagnosis.

For experienced cattle owners, diagnosis becomes more analytical and precise. Subtle changes, patterns over time, and interactions between different factors provide deeper insights into herd health.

The goal is not to replace professional expertise, but to develop a level of awareness that supports timely decision-making.

Chapter 10

Handling, Behavior, and Welfare

Effective handling of Ayrshire cattle begins with understanding how they think, react, and interact with their environment. Behavior and welfare are closely connected—how cattle are handled directly influences their stress levels, productivity, and overall well-being. Ayrshires, known for their alert and active temperament, respond particularly well to calm, consistent, and informed handling.

This chapter explores the psychological foundations of cattle behavior, practical handling techniques, methods to reduce stress, herd dynamics, and the ethical standards that guide responsible cattle ownership. Whether you are a beginner learning basic interaction or a professional refining advanced systems, these principles will help you create a safe, humane, and efficient working environment.

Understanding Cattle Psychology

Cattle behavior is shaped by instinct, environment, and experience. At the core of their psychology is a prey-animal mindset, which means they are naturally alert to potential threats and rely on instinctive responses for safety.

One of the most important behavioral concepts is the flight zone. This is the area around an animal that, when entered, causes it to move away. The size of this zone varies depending on the animal's temperament and previous handling experiences. Calm, well-handled cattle tend to have smaller flight zones, while less accustomed animals may react more quickly and at greater distances.

Another key concept is the point of balance, typically located near the shoulder. Understanding this point allows handlers to guide movement effectively. Moving behind the point of balance encourages forward motion, while stepping ahead of it causes the animal to slow or stop.

Cattle also rely heavily on vision and perception. Their field of vision is wide, allowing them to detect movement easily, but their depth perception is limited. Sudden changes in light, shadows, or unfamiliar objects can cause hesitation or fear.

Memory and learning play a significant role in behavior. Cattle remember both positive and negative experiences. Consistent, calm handling builds trust over time, while rough or inconsistent treatment can lead to long-term resistance or fear.

For beginners, understanding these basic principles provides a foundation for effective handling. For experienced handlers, deeper insight into behavioral patterns allows for more precise and efficient interaction.

Safe Handling Techniques

Safety is a priority in all cattle operations—for both the animals and the handlers. Proper handling techniques reduce the risk of injury and create a more controlled and predictable environment.

The most effective approach to handling is calm and deliberate movement. Sudden actions or loud noises can startle cattle and trigger defensive responses. Moving slowly and maintaining a steady presence helps keep animals relaxed.

Positioning is critical. Handlers should remain aware of their location relative to the animal's flight zone and point of balance. By adjusting position rather than applying force, movement can be guided naturally.

Using clear pathways and controlled spaces supports safe handling. Animals move more confidently when they have a clear direction and minimal distractions. Avoiding sharp turns, dead ends, or visual obstructions helps maintain flow.

Group handling is often more effective than isolating individuals. Cattle feel more secure in a group and are less likely to become agitated when moving together. However, handlers should remain attentive to individual behavior within the group.

Physical contact should be minimal and purposeful. Tools such as gates or panels can assist in guiding movement without direct force. The goal is to influence behavior rather than control it through pressure.

For beginners, focusing on calm movement and proper positioning is the most important step. For professionals, handling becomes more refined, with attention to timing, flow, and subtle behavioral cues.

Stress Reduction Methods

Stress has a direct impact on cattle performance, behavior, and overall welfare. Reducing stress is not only a humane practice but also a practical strategy for improving efficiency and outcomes.

One of the most effective methods of stress reduction is consistency. Predictable routines and familiar environments help cattle feel secure. Sudden changes or disruptions can lead to confusion and anxiety.

Environmental stability also plays a role. Clean, organized spaces with minimal noise and disturbance support calm behavior. Avoiding overcrowding and maintaining clear pathways contribute to a more relaxed atmosphere.

Handling techniques are closely linked to stress levels. Gentle, patient interaction reduces fear and builds trust. Repeated exposure to calm handling helps cattle become more accustomed to human presence.

Minimizing isolation is another important factor. Cattle are social animals, and separation from the herd can cause distress. When individual handling is necessary, maintaining visual or physical contact with other animals can help reduce anxiety.

Observation is key to managing stress. Signs such as rapid movement, vocalization, or resistance indicate that stress levels are increasing. Recognizing these signals allows for timely adjustments.

For beginners, the focus should be on avoiding common stress triggers such as noise and abrupt movement. For experienced handlers, stress reduction becomes a proactive process, integrating environment, routine, and behavior into a cohesive system.

Herd Social Structure

Ayrshire cattle, like all cattle, operate within a structured social system. Understanding herd dynamics is essential for managing behavior and maintaining stability.

Herds naturally establish a hierarchy, where individuals occupy different positions within the group. This hierarchy influences movement, access to resources, and overall interaction. Dominant animals often lead movement and establish patterns that others follow.

Social bonds also play a role. Cattle form relationships within the herd, and these connections influence behavior. Disrupting these bonds can lead to temporary instability as the group adjusts.

Movement within the herd is often collective. Cattle prefer to move together, following established leaders or responding to group cues. This behavior can be used to guide movement efficiently, as influencing a few individuals can affect the entire group.

Understanding herd dynamics helps in predicting behavior and planning handling strategies. For example, moving animals in a way that aligns with their natural tendencies reduces resistance and improves flow.

For beginners, observing herd behavior provides valuable insights into how cattle interact. For professionals, this understanding allows for more strategic management, using social structure to support efficiency and stability.

Ethical Welfare Standards

Ethical welfare is a fundamental responsibility in cattle ownership. It involves ensuring that animals are treated with respect, care, and consideration for their well-being.

At its core, welfare is about providing conditions that allow cattle to live comfortably and express natural behavior. This includes access to space, freedom of movement, and an environment that supports their physical and psychological needs.

Handling practices should always prioritize minimizing distress and discomfort. This means avoiding unnecessary force, using appropriate techniques, and maintaining a calm approach.

Ethical standards also involve accountability. Owners are responsible for the conditions they create and the outcomes of their management practices. Regular evaluation and willingness to improve are key components of responsible ownership.

Respect for animals extends beyond basic care to include long-term consideration. Decisions should be made with an understanding of their impact on the animal's well-being over time.

For beginners, adopting a mindset of care and responsibility sets the foundation for ethical practice. For professionals, welfare becomes integrated into every aspect of management, influencing decisions at all levels.

Integrating Behavior and Welfare into Daily Practice

The principles of behavior and welfare are most effective when they are consistently applied in daily operations. Integration involves aligning handling techniques, environment, and management practices with the natural tendencies of cattle.

A successful system is one where animals move willingly, respond calmly, and interact predictably. This reduces the need for force, improves efficiency, and enhances overall outcomes.

Training and experience play a significant role. As handlers become more familiar with cattle behavior, their ability to anticipate and guide movement improves. This leads to smoother operations and reduced stress for both animals and handlers.

Continuous observation and adjustment ensure that the system remains effective. Behavior is influenced by many factors, and flexibility allows for adaptation to changing conditions.

Chapter 11

Breeding and Reproduction Management

Breeding and reproduction management are central to the sustainability and long-term success of any Ayrshire cattle operation. While milk production often receives the most attention, consistent reproductive performance is what ensures continuity, genetic improvement, and herd stability. A well-managed breeding system combines observation, planning, and strategic decision-making to achieve predictable and efficient results.

This chapter provides a structured and practical guide to understanding reproductive cycles, detecting heat, choosing between natural breeding and artificial insemination, selecting breeding stock, improving genetics, and managing pregnancy. The goal is to equip both beginners and experienced cattle owners with the knowledge needed to make informed and effective breeding decisions.

Heat Detection and Reproductive Cycles

Understanding the reproductive cycle is the foundation of successful breeding. Ayrshire cattle, like other dairy breeds, follow a regular cycle that determines when they are receptive to breeding.

The reproductive cycle typically spans approximately 18 to 24 days, with variations depending on the individual animal. Within this cycle, there is a specific period known as estrus (heat), during which the cow is receptive and capable of conceiving.

Key Signs of Heat

Recognizing heat accurately is essential for timing breeding correctly. Common signs include:

- Increased activity or restlessness
- Mounting behavior or allowing other animals to mount
- Clear mucus discharge
- Changes in vocalization
- Temporary reduction in production or routine behavior

Among these, standing to be mounted is considered one of the most reliable indicators of true heat.

Timing and Observation

Heat periods are relatively short, often lasting between 12 to 24 hours. This makes timing critical. Missing this window can delay breeding and disrupt reproductive efficiency.

Observation should be conducted multiple times daily, especially during periods when animals are most active. Early morning and late evening are often the most effective times for detecting behavioral changes.

For beginners, learning to recognize these signs may take time, but consistent observation builds confidence. For professionals, heat detection becomes more precise, often supported by records and patterns within the herd.

Natural Breeding vs Artificial Insemination

Choosing the right breeding method is a strategic decision that depends on goals, resources, and operational scale. The two primary approaches are natural breeding and artificial insemination (AI).

Natural Breeding

Natural breeding involves the use of a bull to service cows directly.

Advantages:

- Simplicity and minimal technical requirements
- Reduced need for precise timing, as the bull detects heat naturally
- Lower initial setup complexity

Limitations:

- Less control over genetics
- Safety considerations when managing bulls
- Potential for uneven breeding outcomes

Natural breeding is often suitable for smaller operations or systems that prioritize simplicity.

Artificial Insemination (AI)

Artificial insemination involves introducing semen from selected bulls through controlled methods.

Advantages:

- Access to superior genetics from a wide range of sources
- Greater control over breeding outcomes
- Reduced need to maintain a bull

Limitations:

- Requires accurate heat detection
- Needs technical skill or professional assistance
- Timing must be precise

AI is widely used in advanced systems due to its ability to support genetic improvement and consistency.

Choosing the Right Approach

For beginners, natural breeding may provide an easier entry point. For professionals, AI offers significant advantages in terms of control and long-term improvement.

Some operations use a combination of both methods, balancing simplicity with strategic advancement.

Selecting Breeding Stock

The quality of breeding stock determines the future of your herd. Selection should be based on clear criteria that align with your goals and the characteristics of the Ayrshire breed.

Key Selection Criteria

- Conformation and structure: Animals should exhibit strong physical traits that support durability and productivity.

- Production performance: Consistent output and efficiency are important indicators of quality.
- Temperament: Calm and manageable animals contribute to smoother operations.
- Lineage and pedigree: Genetic background provides insight into potential performance and reliability.

Selection should focus on balance rather than extremes. Ayrshire cattle are valued for their well-rounded traits, and maintaining this balance is essential.

Avoiding Common Mistakes

- Selecting based on a single trait rather than overall quality

- Ignoring structural weaknesses that may affect long-term performance
- Overlooking temperament and adaptability

For beginners, focusing on visible traits and basic performance indicators is a good starting point. For experienced breeders, selection becomes more analytical, incorporating detailed records and long-term goals.

Genetic Improvement Basics

Genetic improvement is the process of enhancing desirable traits within a herd over time. It is a gradual and cumulative effort that requires planning and consistency.

Core Principles

- Selection pressure: Choosing animals with desirable traits increases the likelihood of those traits appearing in future generations.

- Consistency: Repeated selection over multiple generations leads to noticeable improvement.

- Balance: Avoid focusing too heavily on one trait at the expense of others.

Ayrshire cattle are particularly suited to genetic improvement programs due to their stable and predictable characteristics.

Practical Application

Genetic improvement begins with clear objectives. Whether the goal is increased production, improved structure, or enhanced efficiency, selection decisions should align with these objectives.

Record-keeping plays a crucial role. Tracking performance and lineage provides valuable data that supports informed decisions.

For beginners, improvement may occur gradually through basic selection practices. For professionals, advanced strategies may involve detailed analysis and targeted breeding plans.

Pregnancy Management

Once breeding has been successful, managing pregnancy becomes the next priority. The goal is to ensure that the cow remains stable and supported throughout the gestation period.

Understanding the Gestation Period

The gestation period for cattle is typically around 280 days, though slight variations are normal. This period can be divided into stages, each with specific characteristics and requirements.

Monitoring Progress

Regular observation is essential for tracking pregnancy. Signs of normal progression include:

- Gradual physical changes

- Stable behavior
- Consistent condition

Unexpected changes or irregularities should be noted, as they may indicate potential challenges.

Environmental and Management Considerations

Pregnant animals benefit from a stable and low-stress environment. Sudden changes, overcrowding, or excessive handling can disrupt normal progression.

Movement and activity should be natural and unrestricted, allowing the animal to maintain comfort and balance.

Preparation for Transition

As pregnancy advances, attention should shift toward preparing for the next stage. While specific details are addressed in later chapters, the focus here is on maintaining stability and ensuring that the animal remains in good condition.

For beginners, pregnancy management involves consistent observation and avoiding unnecessary disruptions. For professionals, it becomes a structured process supported by records and planned timelines.

Integrating Breeding into the Overall System

Breeding and reproduction should not be viewed in isolation. They are part of a larger system that includes management, environment, and long-term planning.

A successful breeding program is predictable and repeatable. It aligns with the overall goals of the operation and supports continuous improvement.

Timing, selection, and consistency are the key elements that connect all aspects of reproduction management. When these elements are properly aligned, the system becomes more efficient and reliable.

Chapter 12

Calf Rearing and Young Stock Management

The future of any Ayrshire cattle operation begins with the successful rearing of calves. Early-life management plays a decisive role in determining long-term performance, structural development, and overall herd quality. Calves are highly responsive to their environment and care during the first weeks and months of life, making this stage one of the most critical in the entire production cycle.

This chapter provides a structured, step-by-step approach to calf rearing and young stock management. It is designed to guide beginners through essential practices while offering deeper insights for experienced cattle owners seeking to refine their systems.

Newborn Calf Care

The first hours of a calf's life are the most important. Proper attention during this period sets the foundation for health, growth, and survival.

Immediately after birth, the calf should be observed carefully to ensure it is breathing normally and able to stand. Most calves will attempt to stand within a short time, and this natural behavior should be supported without unnecessary interference.

The next step is ensuring the calf is clean and dry. Drying helps regulate body temperature and prevents early stress. In many cases, the mother will naturally assist with this process, but additional support may be needed in certain conditions.

Navel care is another critical step. The navel should be clean and protected to reduce the risk of contamination. This simple action plays a significant role in preventing early complications.

The calf should also be placed in a safe and comfortable environment, free from hazards and excessive disturbance.

Stability and calmness during this period help the calf adjust to its new surroundings.

For beginners, the key is to follow a simple checklist: breathing, standing, drying, and cleanliness. For experienced handlers, attention to detail and timing ensures that each step is completed efficiently and effectively.

Colostrum Importance

Colostrum is the first milk produced after birth, and it is essential for the calf's early development. It provides a concentrated source of nutrients and immune support that cannot be replicated later.

The most important factor in colostrum management is timing. The calf's ability to absorb these critical components is highest within the first few hours after birth. Delays can significantly reduce effectiveness.

Colostrum delivers:

- Energy to support early activity and temperature regulation
- Nutrients for initial growth
- Immune support that helps protect against early challenges

The quantity and quality of colostrum are equally important. Ensuring that the calf receives an adequate amount early on is one of the most impactful steps in calf management.

For beginners, the focus should be on ensuring early and sufficient intake. For professionals, attention extends to quality assessment and consistency across all calves.

Colostrum is not just a feeding step—it is a critical biological event that influences the calf's future performance.

Housing Systems for Calves

Housing plays a major role in calf development, providing protection, comfort, and a controlled environment for growth.

There are two primary approaches to calf housing: individual housing and group housing.

Individual Housing

In this system, calves are housed separately during early life.

Advantages:

- Easier monitoring of individual behavior and condition
- Reduced competition
- Controlled environment

This approach is often preferred for beginners, as it simplifies management and allows for close observation.

Group Housing

Group housing involves keeping calves together in small groups.

Advantages:

- Encourages social interaction
- Promotes natural behavior
- Can improve adaptability

However, group housing requires careful management to ensure that all calves receive equal attention.

Key Housing Principles

Regardless of the system used, certain principles apply:

- Cleanliness: Housing areas must be kept clean to maintain a healthy environment

- Ventilation: Proper airflow helps regulate temperature and reduce moisture

- Comfort: Bedding and flooring should support rest and movement

- Space: Adequate space prevents overcrowding and supports natural behavior

For beginners, starting with individual housing provides simplicity and control. For advanced systems, group housing can be optimized to balance efficiency and welfare.

Growth Stages

Calf development occurs in distinct stages, each with specific characteristics and requirements. Understanding these stages helps ensure that management practices align with the calf's needs.

Stage 1: Newborn Phase

This stage covers the first few weeks of life.

- Focus is on stability and adaptation
- Calves are highly dependent on early care
- Observation is critical

Stage 2: Early Growth Phase

During this stage, calves begin to develop strength and coordination.

- Increased activity and curiosity
- Gradual development of feeding behavior
- Continued growth and structural development

Stage 3: Transitional Phase

This stage bridges early growth and independence.

- Calves become more self-sufficient
- Social behavior becomes more evident
- Growth continues at a steady pace

Stage 4: Juvenile Development

At this stage, calves transition into young stock.

- Stronger physical structure
- Increased independence
- Preparation for integration into larger systems

Each stage builds upon the previous one, and management should evolve accordingly. For beginners, recognizing these stages provides clarity and direction. For professionals, detailed understanding allows for precise adjustments that enhance development.

Weaning Strategies

Weaning is a significant milestone in calf development, marking the transition from dependency to independence. It must be handled carefully to ensure a smooth and stress-free process.

Understanding Weaning

Weaning involves gradually reducing reliance on early-life nutrition sources while encouraging the calf to adapt to a more independent intake pattern. The process should be gradual rather than abrupt, allowing the calf to adjust without disruption.

Key Weaning Principles

- Timing: Weaning should occur when the calf is physically ready and able to maintain growth independently

- Gradual transition: Reducing dependency over time prevents stress and supports stability

- Observation: Monitoring behavior and condition ensures that the transition is progressing smoothly

Common Weaning Approaches

- Step-down method: Gradually reducing intake over a set period

- Age-based weaning: Transitioning at a predetermined stage

- Condition-based weaning: Adjusting timing based on the calf's development

For beginners, a gradual and simple approach is the most effective. For professionals, weaning strategies may be refined to optimize growth and efficiency.

Avoiding Weaning Challenges

Abrupt changes, poor timing, or lack of observation can lead to stress and setbacks. A well-planned approach ensures that the calf remains stable and continues to develop without interruption.

Integrating Calf Management into the Overall System

Calf rearing is not an isolated process—it is the foundation of the entire herd. Each calf represents future potential, and the quality of early management directly influences long-term outcomes.

Consistency is the key to success. Daily routines, clean environments, and attentive observation create a stable system that supports growth and development.

Record-keeping can also enhance management. Tracking growth, milestones, and observations provides valuable insights and supports continuous improvement.

For beginners, the goal is to establish reliable routines and build confidence. For professionals, the focus shifts to refinement and optimization, ensuring that each calf reaches its full potential.

Chapter 13

Productivity Optimization and Farm Efficiency

Optimizing productivity in an Ayrshire cattle operation is about achieving consistent, high-level performance while using resources efficiently. Productivity is not determined by a single factor but by the interaction of multiple systems—milk output, herd monitoring, data management, land use, and labor organization. When these elements are aligned, the result is a streamlined operation that delivers reliable results with minimal waste.

This chapter focuses on practical, data-driven strategies to improve performance and efficiency. It is designed to help beginners build structured systems while enabling experienced operators to refine and optimize their operations at a higher level.

Improving Milk Yield

Improving milk yield begins with understanding that production is influenced by consistency, environment, and management precision. Ayrshire cattle are naturally efficient producers, and their output can be enhanced by refining the systems that support them.

One of the most important factors is routine consistency. Maintaining stable daily patterns allows animals to perform predictably. Variations in timing, handling, or environment can disrupt output and reduce efficiency.

Comfort and environment also play a major role. Animals that are calm and comfortable are more likely to maintain consistent production. Minimizing disturbances and ensuring a stable environment supports higher yield levels.

Monitoring individual performance is another key strategy. Not all animals produce equally, and identifying variations allows for targeted improvements. Observing trends over time helps determine which animals are performing well and which may require attention.

Advanced operations often focus on incremental improvements rather than dramatic changes. Small adjustments in routine, environment, or management can lead to measurable gains over time.

For beginners, the focus should be on establishing stable routines and observing patterns. For professionals, yield improvement becomes a process of continuous refinement, supported by data and analysis.

Herd Performance Tracking

Tracking herd performance is essential for understanding how the system is functioning and identifying opportunities for improvement. Without measurement, it is difficult to assess progress or make informed decisions.

Performance tracking involves monitoring key indicators across the herd. These may include:

- Milk output levels
- Behavioral patterns
- Growth and development trends
- Reproductive efficiency

The goal is to create a clear picture of overall performance. This allows for comparison over time and helps identify trends that may not be immediately visible.

Consistency in tracking is critical. Data should be collected regularly and in a standardized format. This ensures that comparisons are accurate and meaningful.

For beginners, simple tracking methods such as daily notes or basic logs can provide valuable insights. For advanced systems, digital tools and automated tracking can enhance accuracy and efficiency.

One of the key benefits of performance tracking is the ability to detect early changes. Subtle shifts in output or behavior can signal underlying issues, allowing for timely adjustments.

Record-Keeping Systems

Record-keeping is the backbone of data-driven management. It transforms observations into actionable information, supporting decision-making and long-term planning.

An effective record-keeping system should be organized, consistent, and easy to use. The complexity of the system should match the scale of the operation.

Basic Record-Keeping

For beginners, a simple system may include:

- Individual animal identification
- Daily or periodic production notes

- Key events and observations

The focus is on capturing essential information without creating unnecessary complexity.

Advanced Record-Keeping

For larger or more advanced operations, record-keeping becomes more detailed and integrated. This may include:

- Digital databases or management software
- Performance analytics and trend analysis
- Automated data collection systems

Advanced systems allow for deeper insights and more precise decision-making. They also support long-term planning by providing historical data.

Key Principles

- Accuracy: Records must reflect actual conditions and events
- Consistency: Data should be collected in a uniform manner
- Accessibility: Information should be easy to retrieve and analyze

A common mistake is collecting data without using it effectively. Records should not only be stored but also reviewed and applied to improve performance.

Pasture Optimization

Pasture is a valuable resource in Ayrshire cattle systems, and optimizing its use contributes significantly to overall efficiency.

Effective pasture management ensures that land remains productive and supports consistent performance.

The first step in pasture optimization is organization. Dividing land into manageable sections allows for controlled use and supports rotational systems. This prevents overuse and promotes recovery.

Rotation planning is a key strategy. Moving animals between sections ensures that pasture is used evenly and remains productive. Timing is important, as it determines how effectively each section recovers before being used again.

Monitoring pasture condition is essential. Observing changes in growth, density, and overall quality provides insight into how well the system is functioning. Adjustments can then be made to maintain balance.

Advanced pasture management may involve mapping and scheduling, allowing for precise control over land use. This level of detail supports higher efficiency and sustainability.

For beginners, basic rotation and observation are sufficient to establish a functional system. For professionals, pasture optimization becomes a dynamic process that integrates data and planning.

Labor Efficiency Strategies

Labor is one of the most significant components of any cattle operation. Improving labor efficiency reduces workload, enhances productivity, and supports smoother daily operations.

The foundation of labor efficiency is workflow organization. Tasks should be arranged in a logical sequence, minimizing unnecessary movement and repetition. Clear pathways and structured routines contribute to smoother operations.

Task standardization is another important strategy. Establishing consistent methods for completing tasks ensures that work is performed efficiently and reduces variability.

Time management plays a key role. Identifying peak activity periods and aligning tasks accordingly improves overall efficiency. Breaking down tasks into manageable segments helps maintain focus and productivity.

For larger operations, delegation and coordination become essential. Clear roles and responsibilities ensure that tasks are completed effectively without overlap or confusion.

Advanced systems may incorporate automation and technology to reduce manual labor. This can include equipment that streamlines processes or systems that support monitoring and data collection.

For beginners, the focus should be on simplifying tasks and creating clear routines. For professionals, labor efficiency becomes a strategic priority, with continuous refinement and optimization.

Integrating Systems for Maximum Efficiency

True optimization occurs when all elements—milk production, performance tracking, record-keeping, pasture management, and labor—are integrated into a cohesive system.

Integration begins with alignment of goals. Each component should support the overall objectives of the operation. For example, pasture management should align with production goals, and record-keeping should support decision-making.

Communication between systems is also important. Data collected from one area should inform decisions in another. This creates a feedback loop that supports continuous improvement.

Flexibility is another key factor. Conditions change, and the ability to adapt ensures that the system remains effective. Regular evaluation and adjustment help maintain efficiency over time.

Advanced Optimization Techniques

For experienced operators, optimization extends beyond basic management into more advanced strategies:

- Data analysis: Using historical data to identify trends and predict outcomes
- Benchmarking: Comparing performance against standards or previous results
- Continuous improvement cycles: Regularly evaluating and refining systems
- Precision management: Adjusting practices based on detailed observations and data

These techniques allow for a higher level of control and efficiency, enabling operations to achieve consistent and measurable improvements.

Chapter 14

Troubleshooting Common Problems

Even in well-managed Ayrshire cattle operations, challenges will arise. The difference between a struggling system and a successful one often comes down to how quickly and effectively problems are identified and resolved. Troubleshooting is not guesswork—it is a structured process of observing symptoms, identifying root causes, and applying targeted solutions.

This chapter is designed as a practical, action-oriented guide, using a strict Problem → Cause → Solution format. It focuses on the most common issues encountered in Ayrshire cattle systems and provides clear steps to resolve them efficiently without unnecessary trial and error.

Problem 1: Low Milk Production

Cause

- Inconsistent daily routines
- Poor environmental comfort or disturbances
- Reduced intake or irregular consumption patterns
- Stress from handling or surroundings
- Natural variation between individuals

Solution

- Establish and maintain strict consistency in daily routines, especially timing and workflow
- Evaluate the environment for noise, overcrowding, or disruptions and eliminate stress triggers
- Observe individual animals to identify underperformers and compare with herd averages
- Improve overall comfort and stability, ensuring animals are calm during production periods
- Track production data to identify patterns and adjust management accordingly

Problem 2: Sudden Drop in Milk Output

Cause

- Abrupt changes in routine or environment
- Stress events (movement, noise, unfamiliar conditions)
- Environmental discomfort (temperature changes, poor airflow)
- Disruption in system flow

Solution

- Immediately review recent changes and restore previous stable conditions where possible
- Minimize disturbances and return to predictable routines
- Ensure animals are in a calm, controlled environment
- Monitor affected animals closely to confirm recovery

- Avoid making multiple changes at once—adjust one factor at a time

Problem 3: Feeding-Related Imbalance (Uneven Condition Across Herd)

Cause

- Unequal access to feeding areas
- Dominance behavior within the herd
- Poor distribution of resources
- Inconsistent feeding structure

Solution

- Ensure equal access points so all animals can reach resources without competition
- Observe herd dynamics and identify dominant individuals limiting access
- Spread feeding areas to reduce crowding
- Maintain a consistent and structured feeding system
- Monitor body condition regularly and adjust access accordingly

Problem 4: Reduced Appetite or Irregular Intake Behavior

Cause

- Environmental stress or discomfort
- Sudden changes in routine
- Poor placement of feeding or watering points
- Disruptions in herd structure

Solution

- Check for environmental stress factors such as heat, noise, or overcrowding
- Restore routine consistency and avoid abrupt changes
- Ensure feeding and watering tools are accessible and properly positioned

- Observe individual animals to identify patterns or specific triggers
- Maintain a calm environment to encourage normal intake behavior

Problem 5: Aggression or Behavioral Conflicts

Cause

- Competition for spacc or resources
- Disruption of herd hierarchy
- Overcrowding
- Introduction of new animals without adjustment

Solution

- Increase available space and reduce competition points
- Introduce new animals gradually to allow hierarchy stabilization
- Observe herd interactions and identify aggressive individuals
- Adjust group structure if necessary to maintain balance
- Ensure consistent handling to reduce stress-induced aggression

Problem 6: Resistance to Handling or Movement

Cause

- Previous negative handling experiences
- Poorly designed movement pathways
- Fear of unfamiliar environments or objects
- Inconsistent handling techniques

Solution

- Use calm, consistent handling methods and avoid force
- Improve pathways to ensure clear, unobstructed movement
- Remove visual distractions such as shadows or sudden light changes
- Build familiarity through repeated, positive interaction

- Work with herd behavior rather than against it, using natural movement patterns

Problem 7: Environmental Stress (Heat or Cold Impact)

Cause

- Exposure to extreme temperatures
- Lack of shade or protection
- Poor ventilation or airflow
- Inadequate shelter positioning

Solution

- Provide adequate shelter and protection from environmental extremes

- Improve airflow in enclosed areas to maintain stable conditions

- Adjust activity patterns to avoid peak stress periods

- Monitor animal behavior for signs of discomfort and respond quickly

- Ensure consistent access to water to support temperature regulation

Problem 8: Uneven Herd Performance

Cause

- Variation in individual genetics and capacity
- Differences in access to resources
- Inconsistent management practices
- Lack of performance tracking

Solution

- Implement basic performance tracking to identify trends
- Group animals based on performance levels where possible
- Ensure equal access to resources across the herd
- Adjust management practices to support underperforming individuals

- Focus on consistency across all areas of the system

Problem 9: Poor Pasture Utilization

Cause

- Overgrazing in certain areas
- Underutilization of other sections
- Poor rotation planning
- Inefficient movement between sections

Solution

- Divide pasture into clearly defined sections for controlled use

- Implement a rotational system to balance grazing pressure

- Monitor pasture condition regularly and adjust usage

- Improve access pathways to ensure smooth movement

- Avoid leaving animals in one area for too long

Problem 10: Water Access Issues

Cause

- Insufficient number of water points

- Poor placement causing crowding
- Inconsistent supply or system failure
- Contamination or poor maintenance

Solution

- Ensure multiple access points to reduce competition
- Position water sources strategically across the system
- Regularly check and maintain supply systems
- Keep water sources clean and accessible
- Observe usage patterns to identify and correct imbalances

Problem 11: Recurring Issues Without Clear Cause

Cause

- Lack of structured observation
- Inconsistent record-keeping
- Multiple overlapping factors
- Failure to identify patterns

Solution

- Begin tracking key data points consistently (production, behavior, environment)

- Look for patterns over time rather than isolated events
- Break down the problem into smaller components and analyze each one
- Adjust one variable at a time to identify cause-and-effect relationships
- Maintain detailed notes to support future decision-making

Problem 12: System Inefficiency (High Effort, Low Output)

Cause

- Poor workflow organization
- Unnecessary movement or repetition
- Lack of coordination between systems
- Ineffective use of available resources

Solution

- Analyze daily routines and eliminate unnecessary steps
- Organize tasks into a logical sequence
- Align equipment, pathways, and processes to support efficiency
- Use observation and data to identify bottlenecks

- Continuously refine the system for smoother operation

Diagnosing Recurring Issues: A Structured Approach

Recurring problems require a more analytical approach. Instead of reacting to symptoms, focus on identifying patterns and root causes.

Step 1: Observe

Carefully monitor the situation and gather as much information as possible. Look for consistent signs or repeated behaviors.

Step 2: Identify Patterns

Determine whether the issue occurs at specific times, under certain conditions, or with particular animals.

Step 3: Isolate Variables

Change one factor at a time to see how it affects the outcome. Avoid making multiple adjustments simultaneously.

Step 4: Apply Targeted Solutions

Once the cause is identified, implement a focused solution and monitor the results.

Step 5: Evaluate and Adjust

Assess whether the solution is effective. If not, revisit the process and refine your approach.

This structured method ensures that problems are addressed logically and efficiently, reducing trial-and-error and improving outcomes.

Chapter 15

Costs, Budgeting, and Long-Term Responsibility

Ayrshire cattle ownership is both a financial investment and a long-term commitment that extends beyond simple operational management. While previous chapters have explored the technical and practical aspects of raising and managing Ayrshire cattle, this final chapter brings everything together through a financial and ethical lens. Success in cattle ownership is not only measured by productivity but also by sustainability, responsibility, and the ability to maintain a stable system over time.

Understanding costs, planning effectively, and embracing ethical responsibility are essential for building an operation that is resilient, efficient, and rewarding. This chapter provides a comprehensive perspective on the financial structure of Ayrshire cattle ownership and the long-term mindset required to sustain it.

Initial Setup Costs

The foundation of any Ayrshire cattle operation begins with the initial investment. These costs represent the starting point of your system and often determine the scale and structure of your operation.

Initial setup costs typically include:

- Acquisition of animals
- Land preparation and allocation
- Infrastructure development
- Essential equipment and tools

These investments should be approached strategically rather than impulsively. The goal is not simply to acquire resources but to build a system that aligns with your long-term objectives.

One of the most common mistakes is underestimating startup costs. Beginners often focus on visible expenses while overlooking indirect or supporting costs. A well-planned budget accounts for both immediate and secondary requirements.

Another key consideration is scalability. Designing your setup with future growth in mind prevents the need for costly restructuring later. Even small operations benefit from planning that allows for expansion or adjustment.

For experienced operators, initial investments are often guided by optimization —allocating resources in a way that maximizes efficiency and long-term returns.

Monthly and Yearly Expenses

Once the operation is established, ongoing expenses become the primary financial focus. These recurring costs determine the sustainability of the system and must be carefully managed.

Monthly and yearly expenses may include:

- Operational inputs and supplies
- Maintenance of infrastructure and equipment
- Labor and time investment
- Utilities and resource usage

The key to managing these expenses is consistency and predictability. Understanding how costs fluctuate over time allows for better planning and reduces the risk of unexpected financial strain.

Seasonal variation is an important factor. Certain periods may require increased expenditure, while others may be more stable. Anticipating these fluctuations ensures that resources are allocated effectively.

For beginners, tracking expenses in a simple and organized manner is essential. Even basic records provide valuable insights into spending patterns.

For professionals, expense management becomes more analytical. Identifying areas of inefficiency and implementing adjustments can significantly improve overall performance.

Equipment Replacement Planning

Equipment is a long-term investment, but it is not permanent. Over time, wear and usage will require replacement or upgrading. Planning for this process is a critical component of financial stability.

Equipment replacement should be approached as a scheduled and predictable process, rather than a reactive one. Waiting until equipment fails can lead to disruptions and higher costs.

Key considerations include:

- Lifespan of equipment
- Frequency of use
- Maintenance history

By understanding these factors, you can estimate when replacement will be necessary and allocate resources accordingly.

A structured approach involves setting aside funds over time, creating a replacement reserve. This ensures that when the time comes, the financial impact is manageable.

For beginners, even a simple plan for future replacement provides a significant advantage. For advanced operations, detailed tracking and forecasting allow for precise planning and minimal disruption.

Emergency Budgeting

No operation is immune to unexpected events. Emergencies can arise from environmental conditions, system failures, or unforeseen challenges. Preparing for these situations is essential for maintaining stability.

Emergency budgeting involves creating a financial buffer that can absorb sudden costs without compromising the overall operation.

This buffer should be:

- Accessible for immediate use
- Sufficient to cover unexpected expenses
- Separate from regular operational funds

The size of the emergency fund depends on the scale of the operation and the level of risk involved. Larger systems may require more substantial reserves, while smaller setups can operate with more modest buffers.

A common mistake is assuming that emergencies are unlikely or infrequent. In reality, they are an inevitable part of long-term operations. Preparation reduces their impact and ensures continuity.

For beginners, building even a small reserve is a strong starting point. For professionals, emergency planning is integrated into the overall financial strategy.

Profitability Considerations

Profitability is not simply about generating income—it is about achieving a balance between input and output that supports long-term sustainability.

Ayrshire cattle are known for their efficiency, which provides a strong foundation for profitability. However, realizing this potential requires careful management.

Key factors influencing profitability include:

- Consistency of production
- Efficiency of resource use
- Control of expenses
- Quality of output

Profitability should be viewed as a long-term outcome, rather than a short-term goal. Fluctuations are normal, and success depends on maintaining balance over time.

For beginners, the focus should be on establishing a stable system that covers costs and builds experience. For professionals, profitability becomes a matter of refinement—optimizing systems to improve margins and efficiency.

It is important to avoid overemphasis on immediate returns. Decisions should be made with consideration for their long-term impact, ensuring that short-term gains do not compromise future stability.

Ethical Ownership and Responsibility

Beyond financial considerations, Ayrshire cattle ownership carries a significant ethical responsibility. Animals depend entirely on their owners for care, environment, and well-being. This responsibility extends beyond productivity to include respect, humane treatment, and long-term commitment.

Ethical ownership involves:

- Providing appropriate living conditions
- Ensuring humane handling and treatment
- Making decisions that prioritize well-being
- Maintaining accountability for outcomes

Ethics are not separate from management—they are integrated into every decision. A system that prioritizes welfare often leads to better performance, as animals that are treated well are more likely to perform consistently.

Responsibility also includes environmental awareness. Sustainable practices support not only the operation but also the broader ecosystem.

For beginners, adopting an ethical mindset from the start establishes a strong foundation. For professionals, ethics become a guiding principle that shapes long-term strategy and reputation.

Long-Term Commitment

Ayrshire cattle ownership is not a short-term endeavor. It requires a commitment that extends over years, encompassing growth, challenges, and continuous improvement.

Long-term success depends on:

- Consistency in management
- Adaptability to changing conditions
- Willingness to learn and improve
- Patience and persistence

Cattle systems evolve over time. What begins as a simple operation can grow into a complex and refined system. This evolution requires ongoing attention and a willingness to adjust.

Commitment also involves recognizing that success is built gradually. Each decision contributes to the overall outcome, and progress is achieved through steady, deliberate effort.

For beginners, understanding the long-term nature of cattle ownership helps set realistic expectations. For professionals, commitment is reflected in the ability to sustain and improve operations over extended periods.